787
EC19

MEL BAY PRESENTS

American Love Songs
& Ballads for
Acoustic Guitar

BY STEVEN ZDENEK ECKELS

Note From the Author

To expedite the learning process, I have made every effort to keep the notation clear and simple. It is important to remember that notation represents the only the basic structure of the music; the nuance and artistry must be added by the performer. When learning this music keep in mind the following:

1. Let all notes sustain unless otherwise indicated.

2. Notes in any given passage may carry different functions, and therefore will be played with different volumes. For example: one note may represent the "melody", another the "bass" and another a "fill note". It is up to the performer to interpret these functions and perform the music accordingly. Of special importance are the "fill notes" that should be played much softer than the melody or the bass. Sometimes they serve as "place holders" for the left hand and are implied, rather than heard.

I have included the basic chord symbols for two reasons. First, in some cases it may speed up the learning process. Secondly, the symbols may be used by other instrumentalists to accompany the guitar solo.

These solos all begin with the theme stated in a "chorale" style. This will enable the performer to learn the left hand fingerings and to hear the melody and bass. It is also the simplest of the variations, and can serve as a complete solo for the intermediate student level. The subsequent variations contain the finger picking arrangements which utilize various fill notes and other variation techniques. These are more challenging technically.

It is my hope that these arrangements are useful and enjoyable for the student, teacher, and recitalist. While these tunes were the first I ever learned (when I was 10 years old), arranging them for finger style guitar was an opportunity to get reacquainted with them in a refreshing and beautiful new way.

Steven Eckels

Contents

Jeanie with the Light Brown Hair

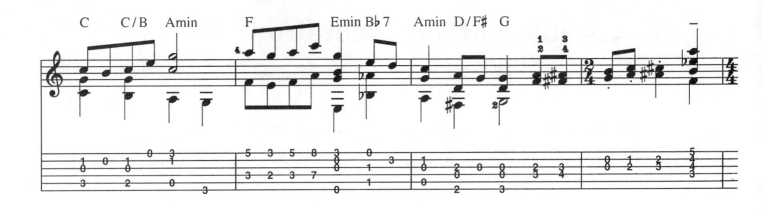

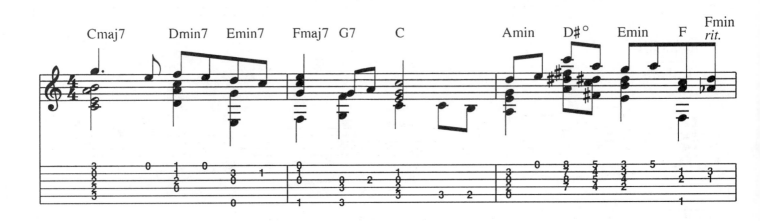

VARIATION I

Moderate stride tempo ♩ = 120

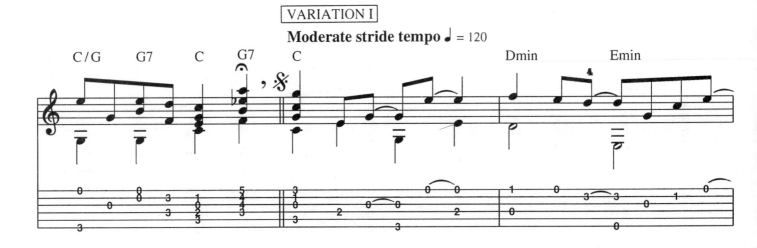

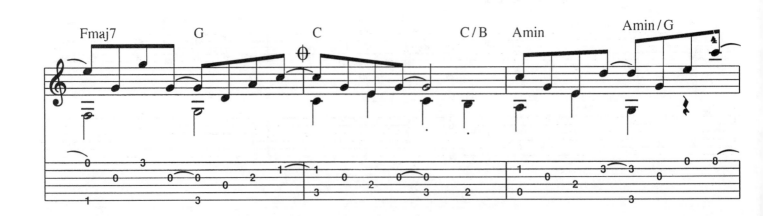

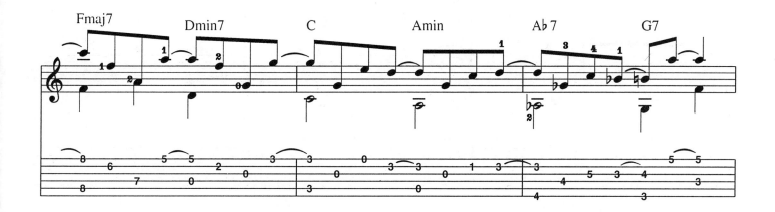

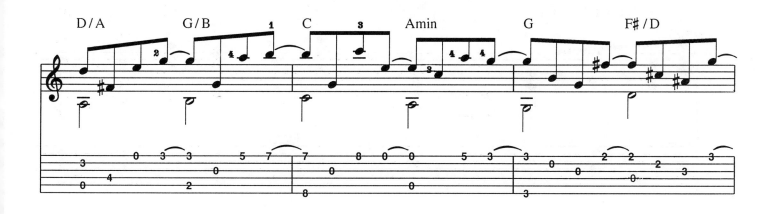

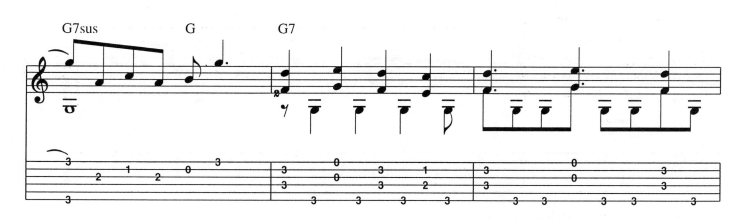

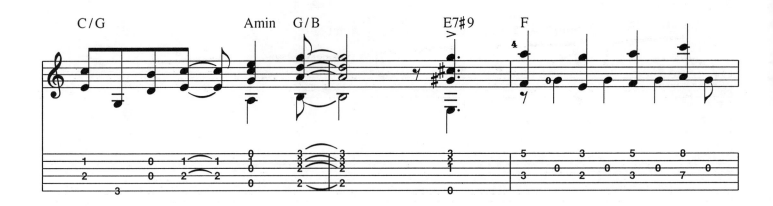

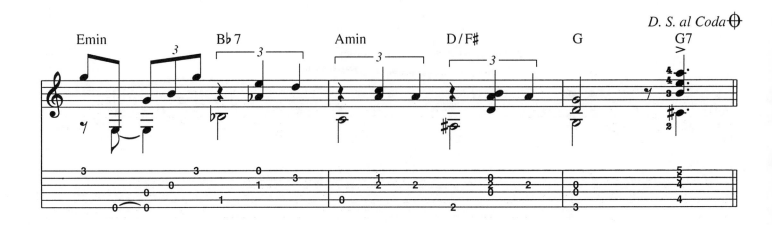

D. S. al Coda ⊕

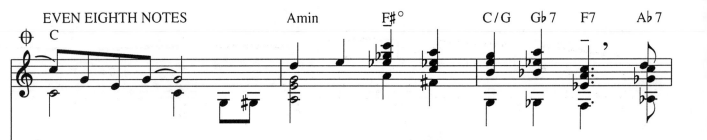

Rubato

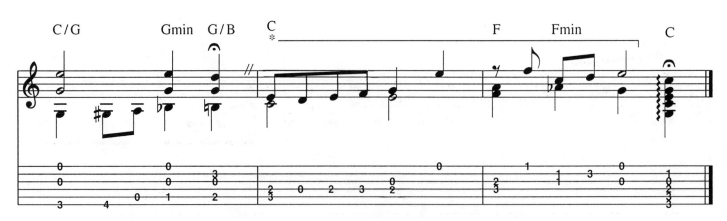

*Melody may be played with artificial harmonics.

Darling Nelly Gray

Freely

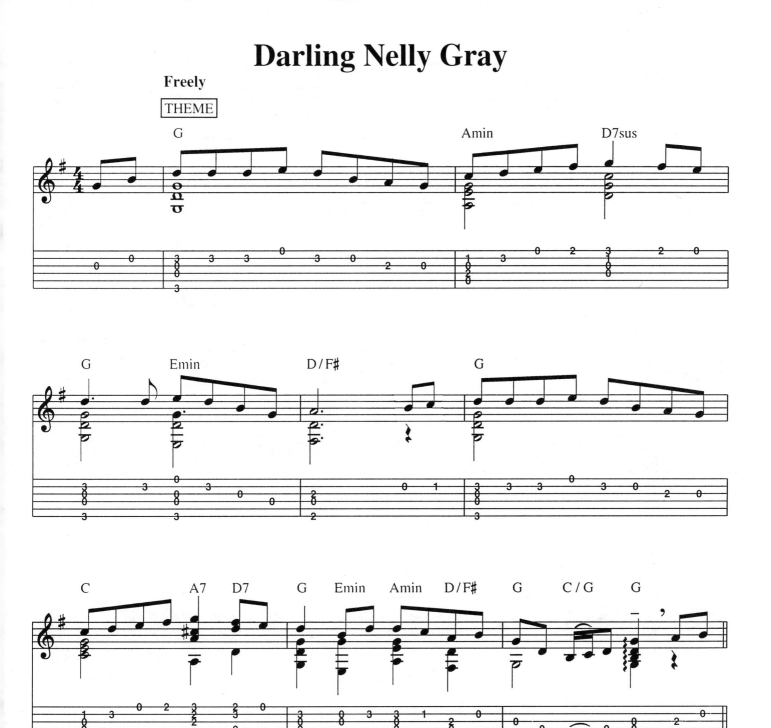

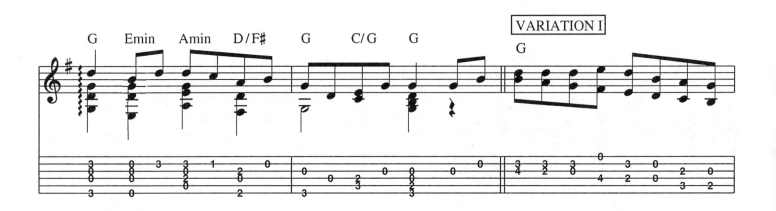

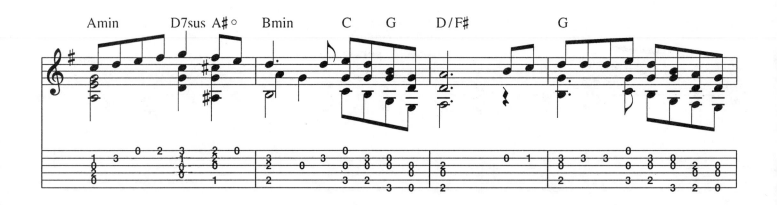

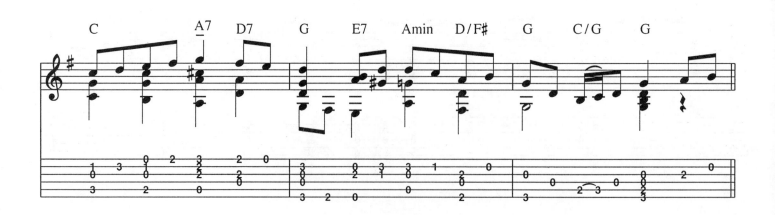

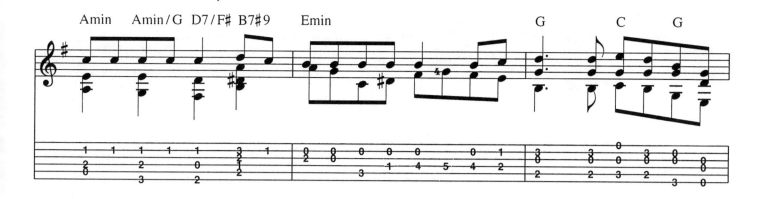

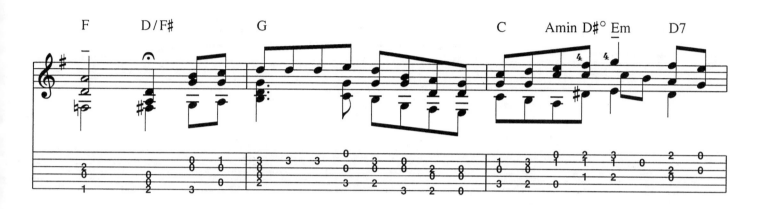

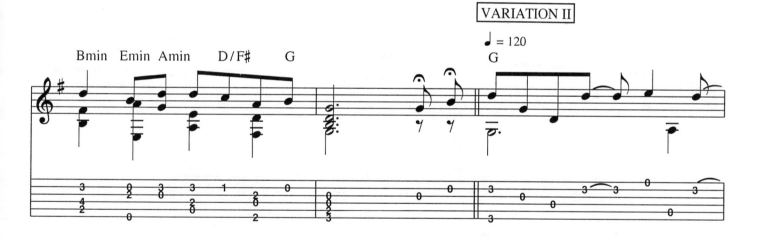

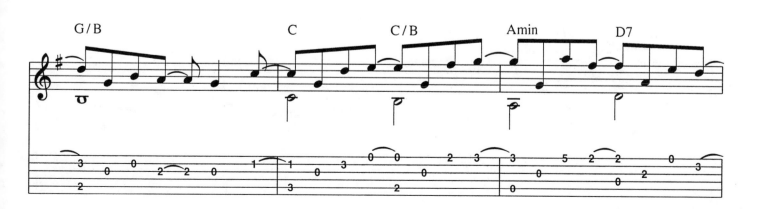

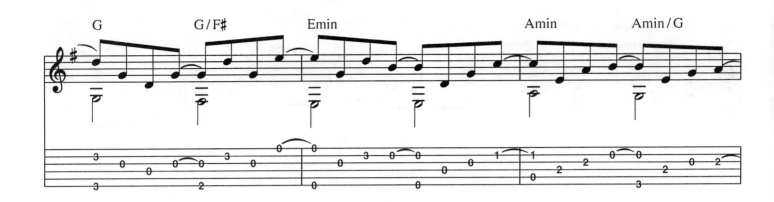

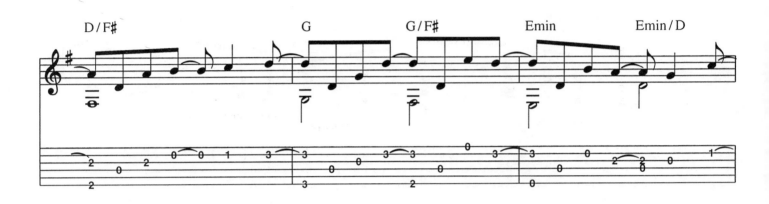

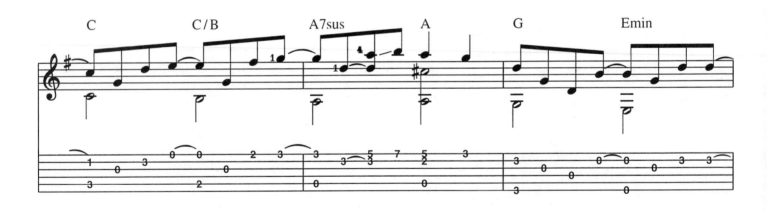

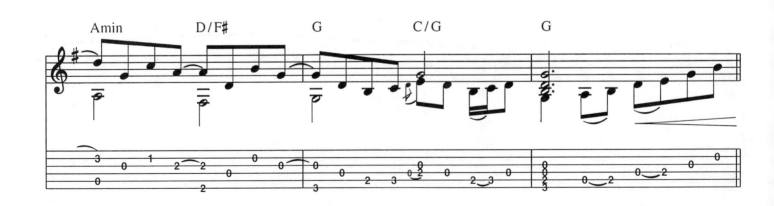

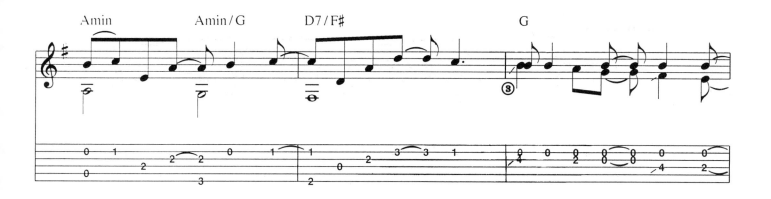

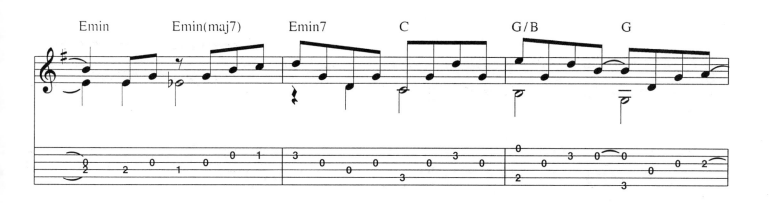

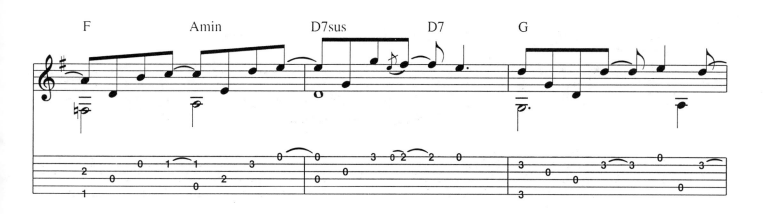

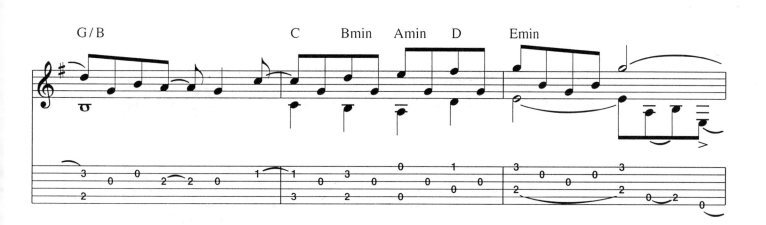

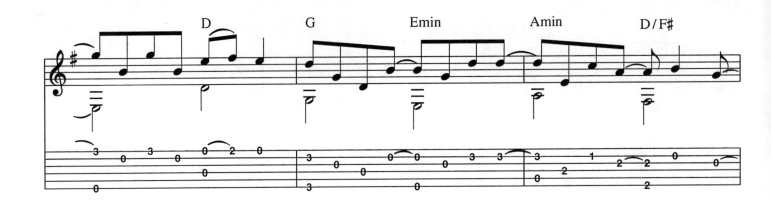

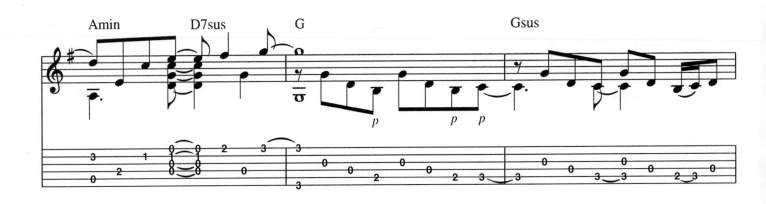

rit. 2nd time

Johnny Has Gone for a Soldier

Freely

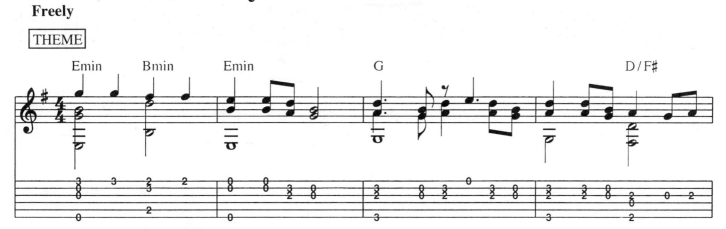

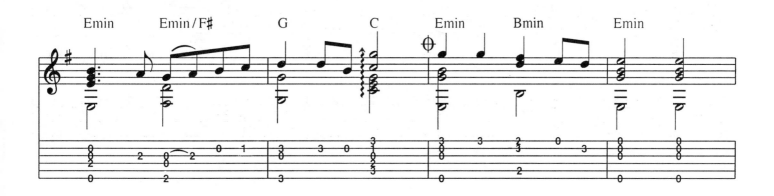

Let "D" ring

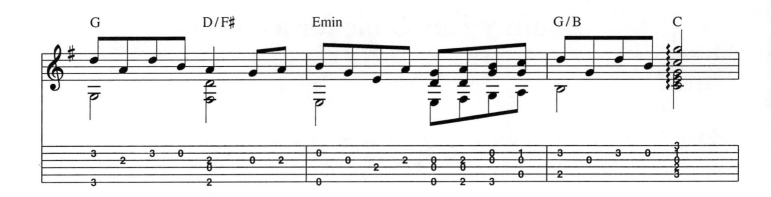

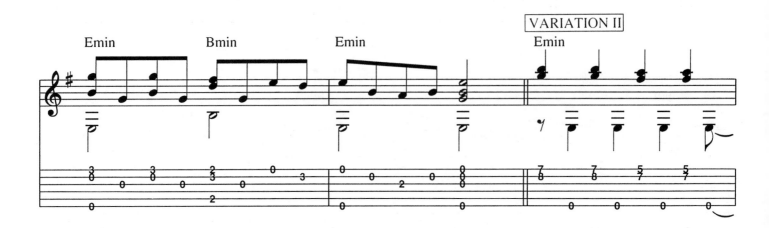

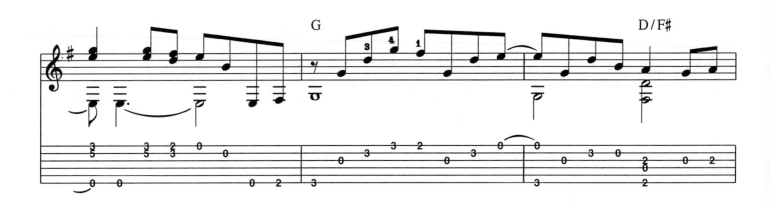

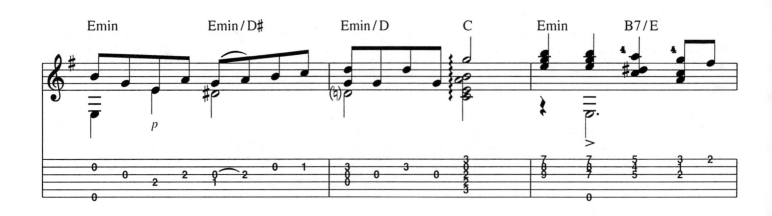

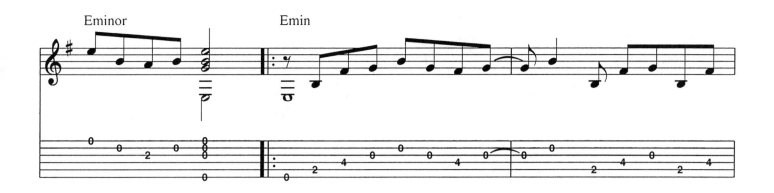

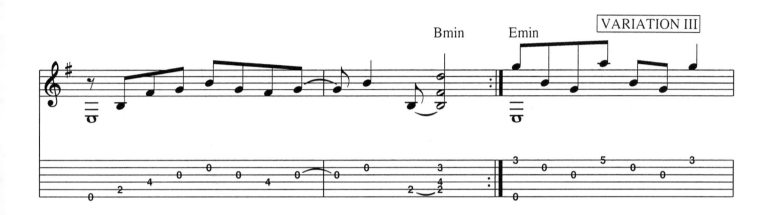

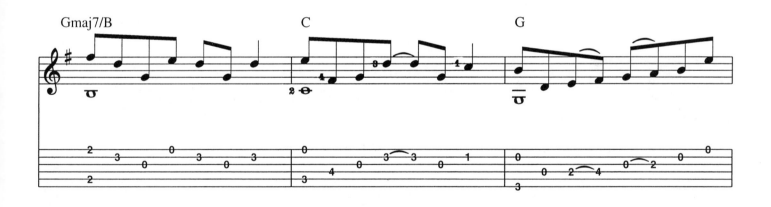

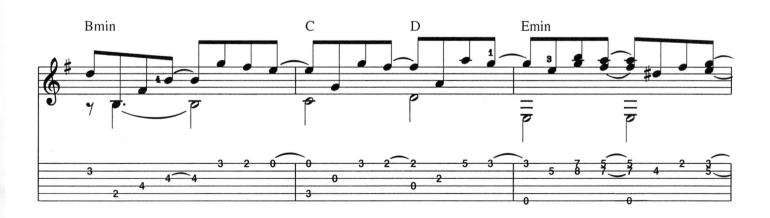

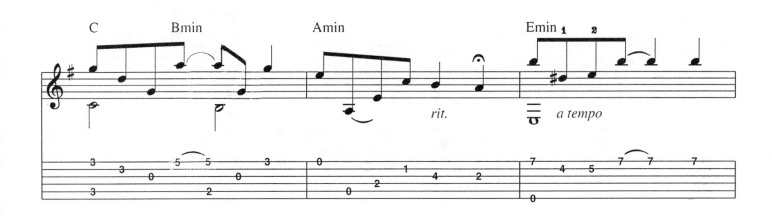

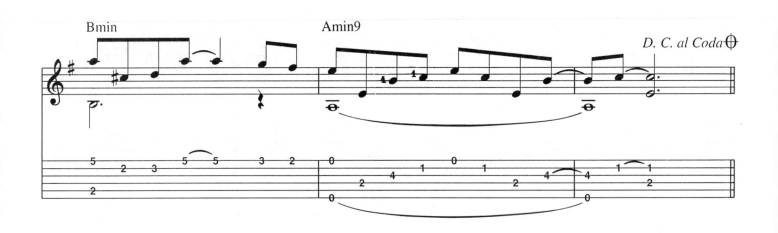

Lily of the West

Freely

THEME

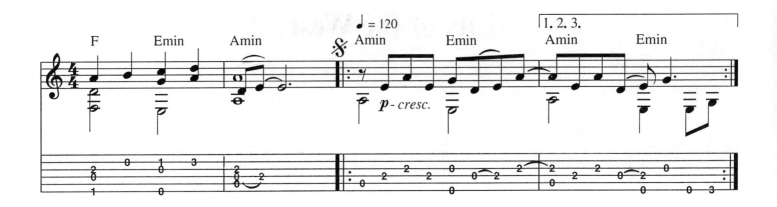

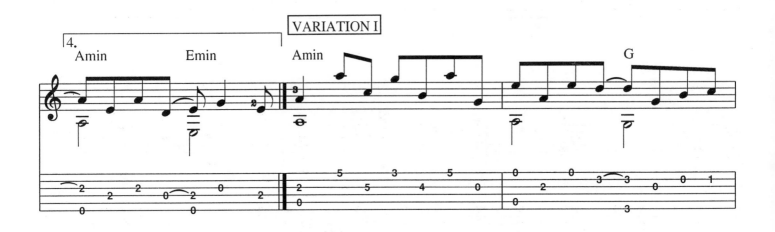

VARIATION I

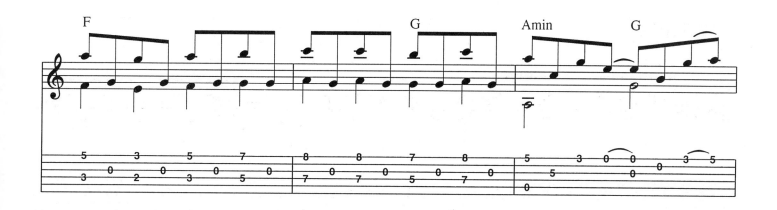

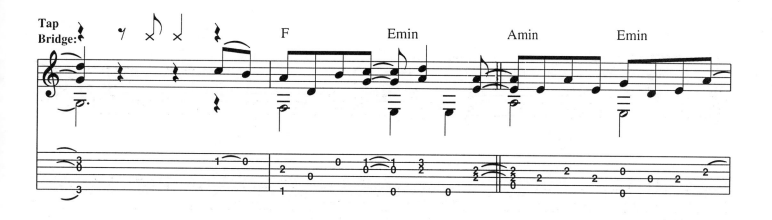

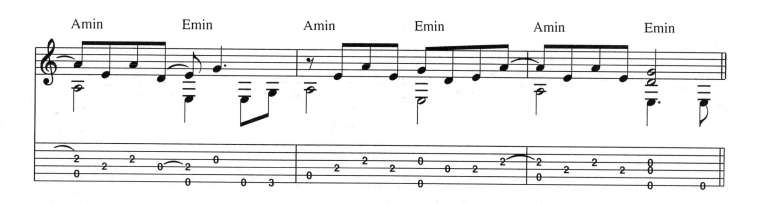

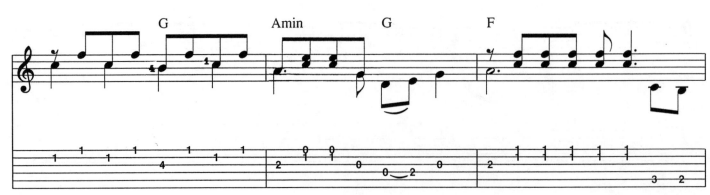

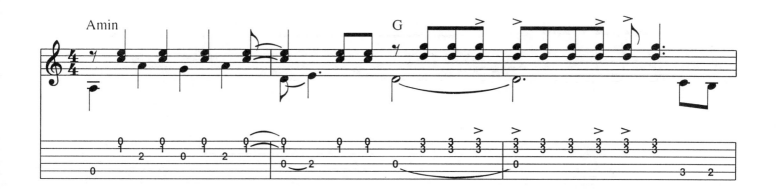

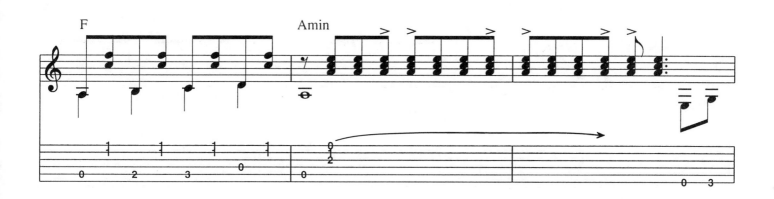

VARIATION III

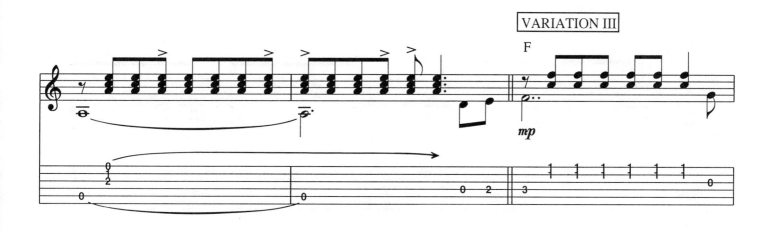

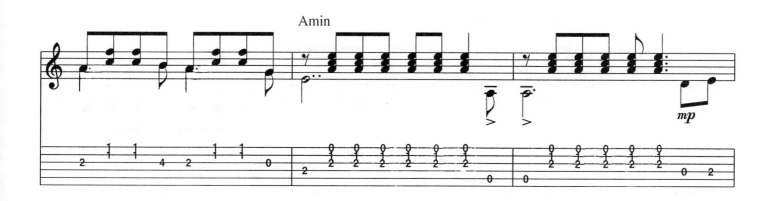

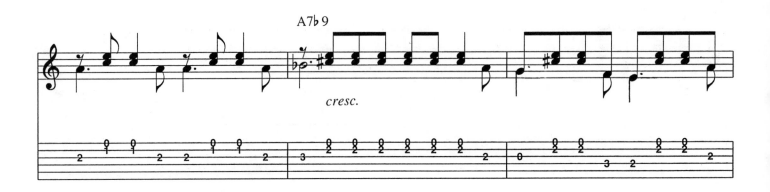

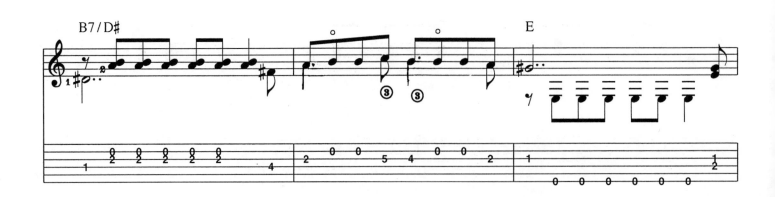

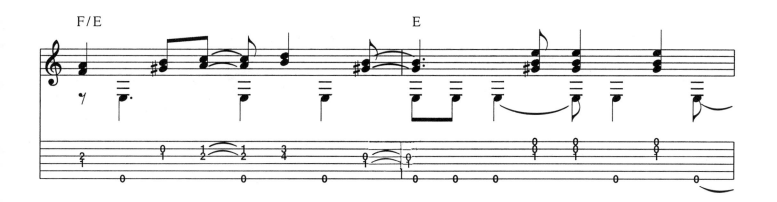

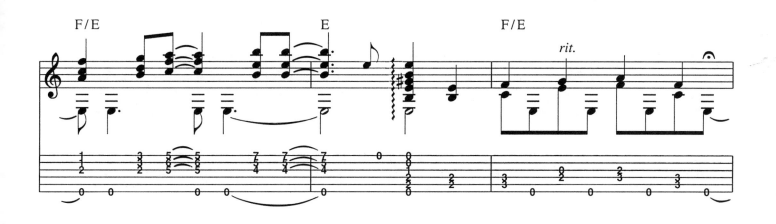

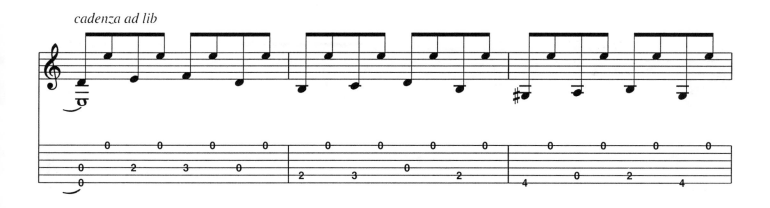

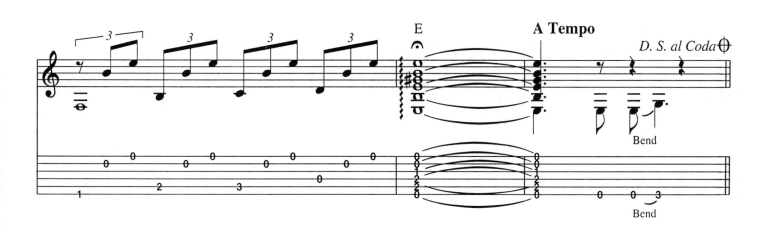

25

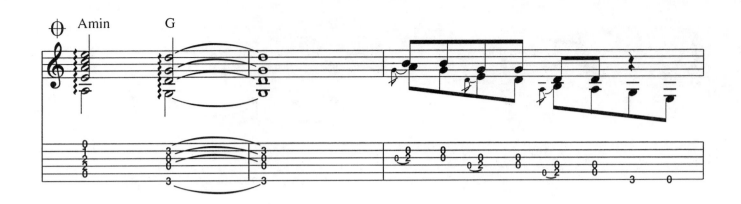

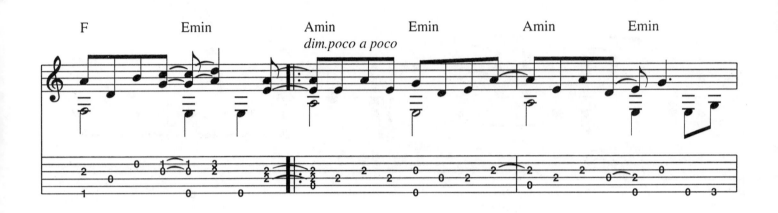

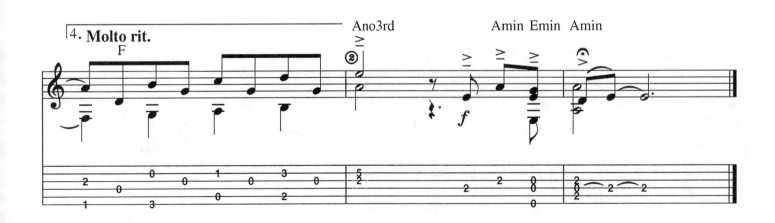

Paper of Pins

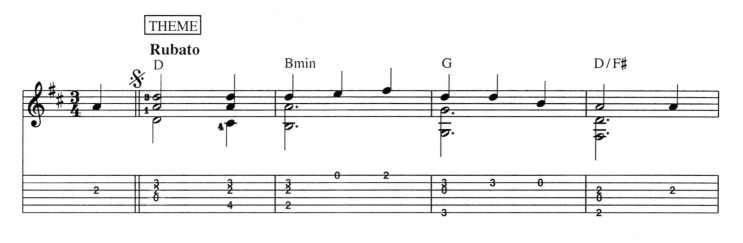

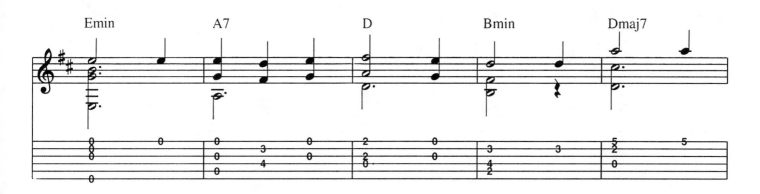

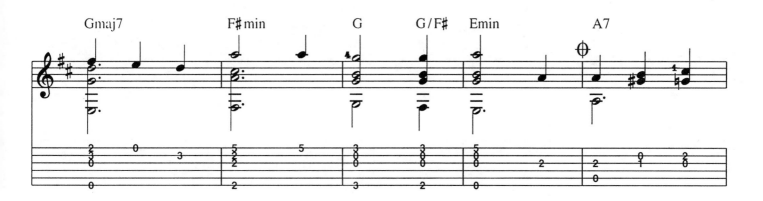

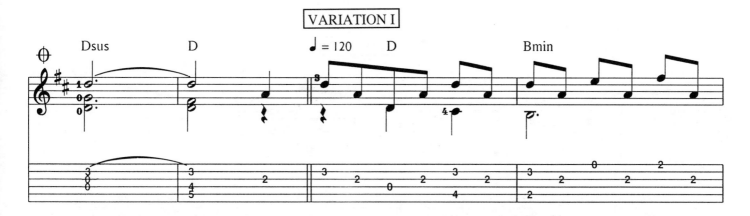

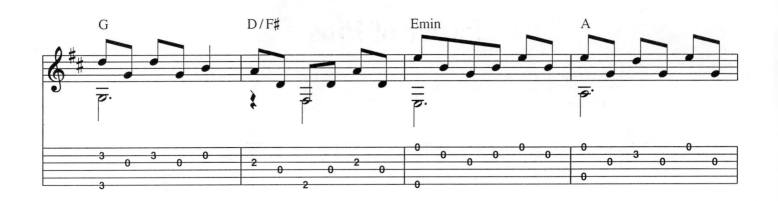

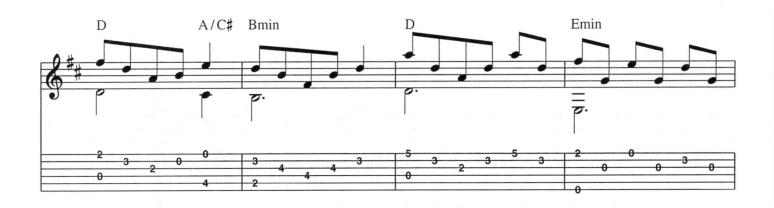

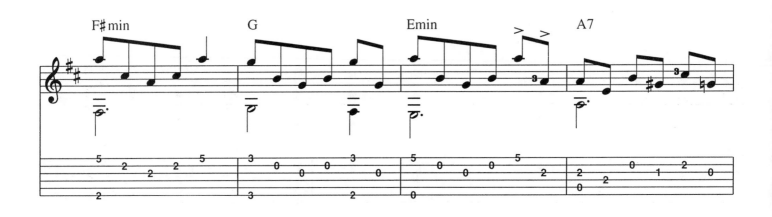

VARIATION II

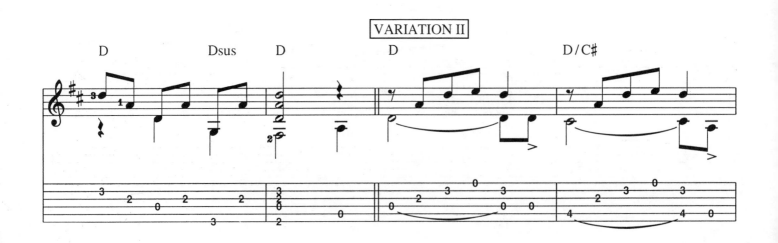

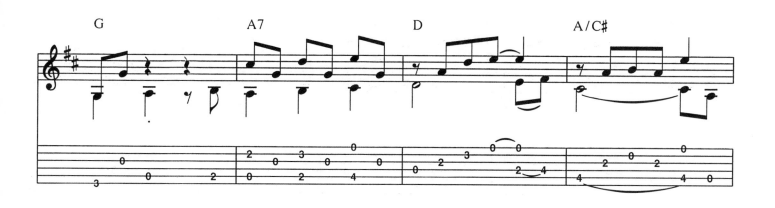

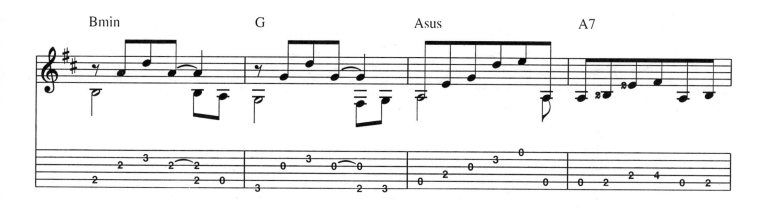

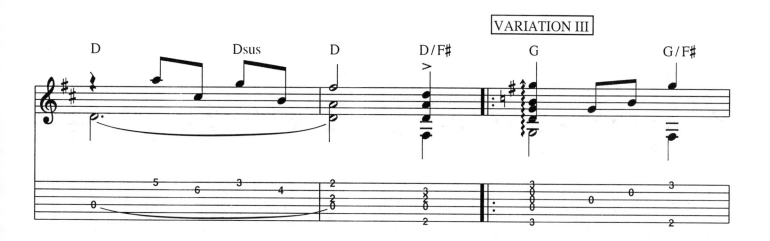

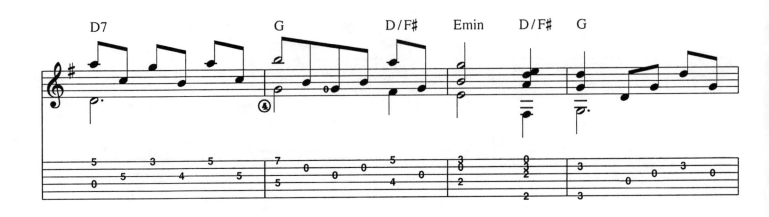

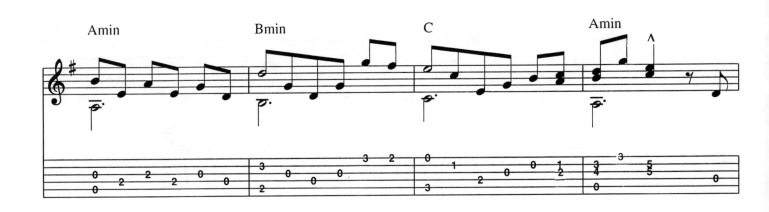

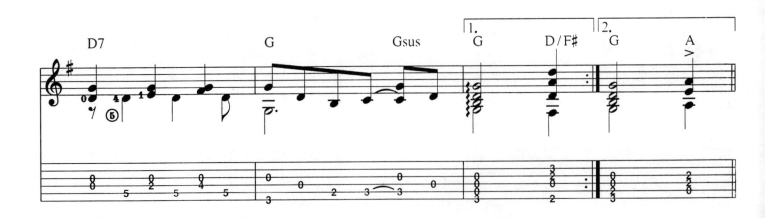

VARIATION IV

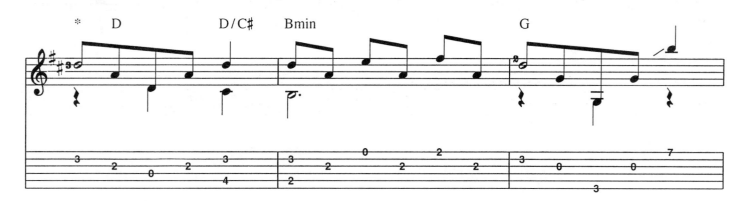

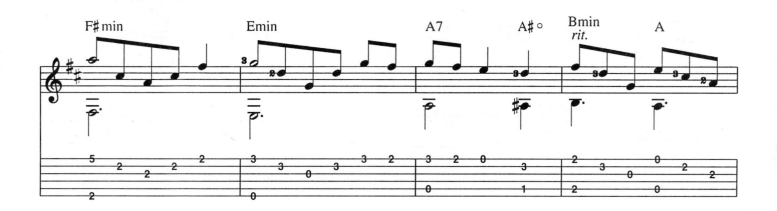

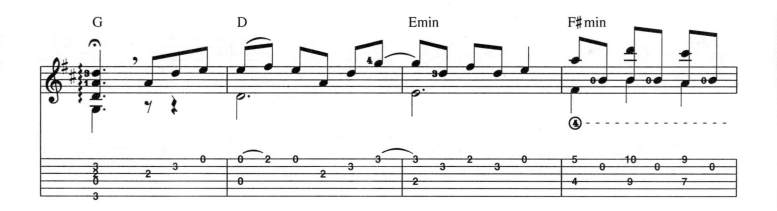

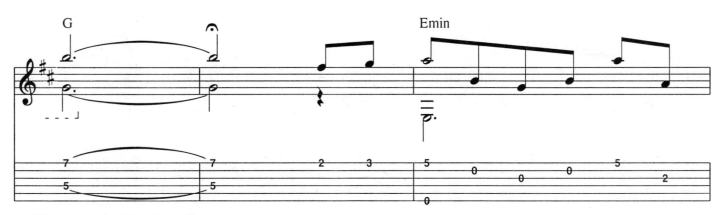

*Mute open A with palm of hand.

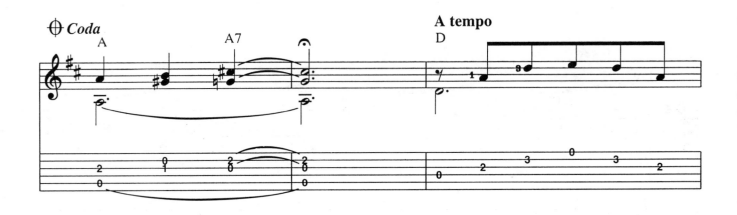

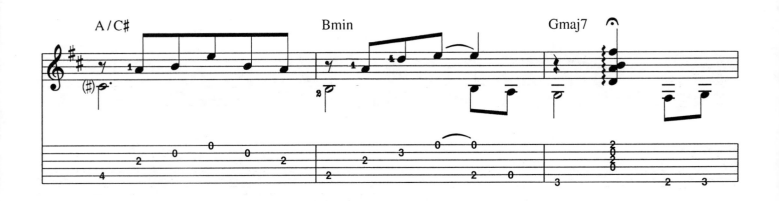

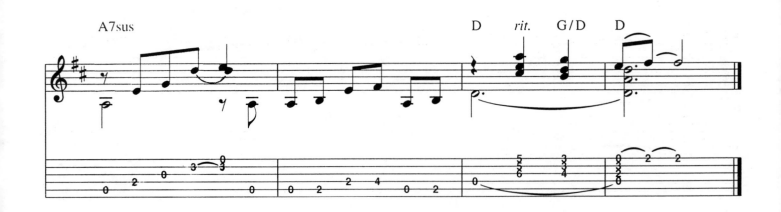

Fair and Tender Ladies

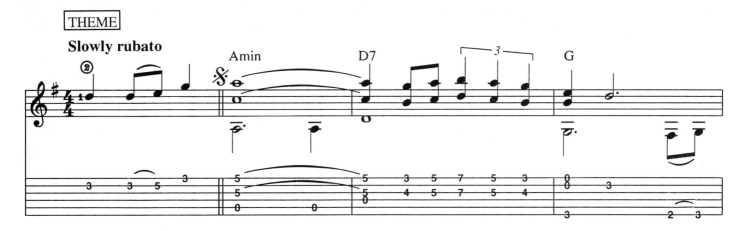

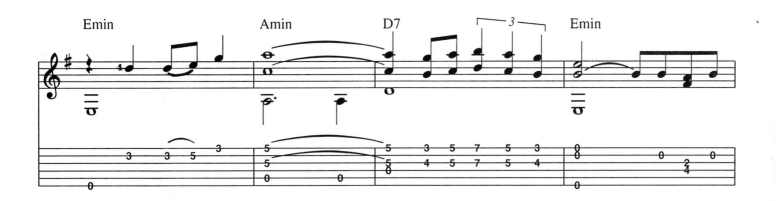

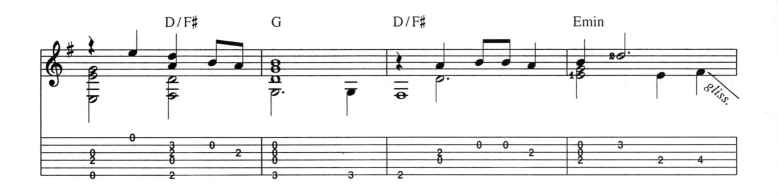

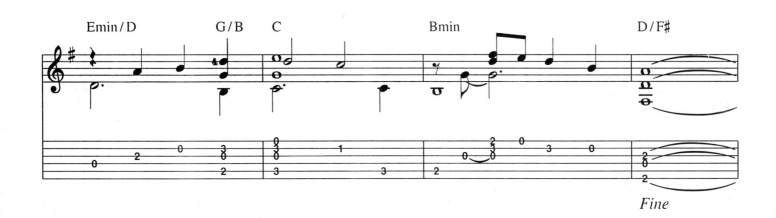

Fine

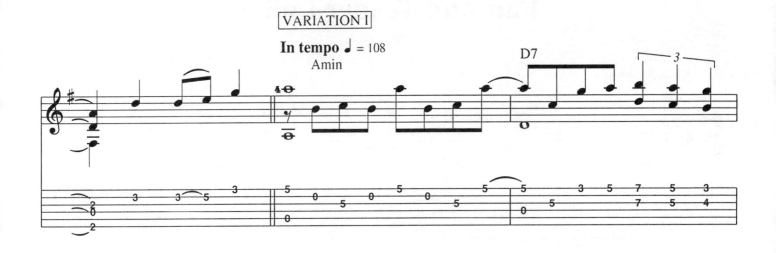

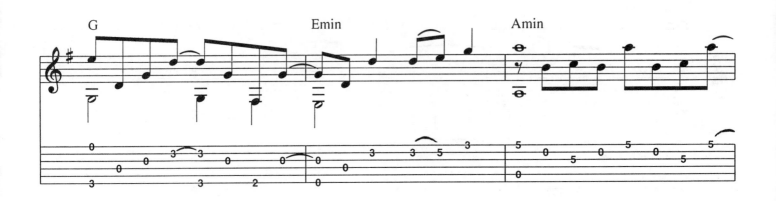

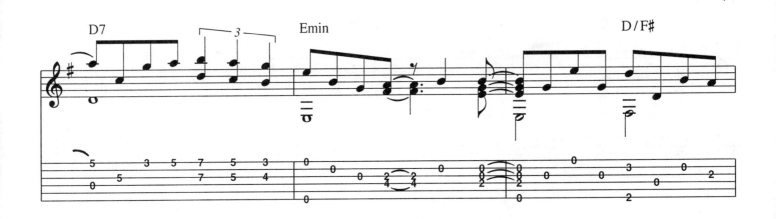

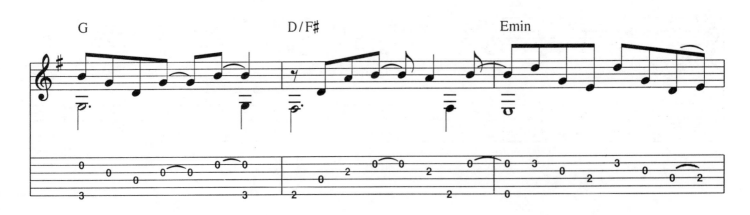

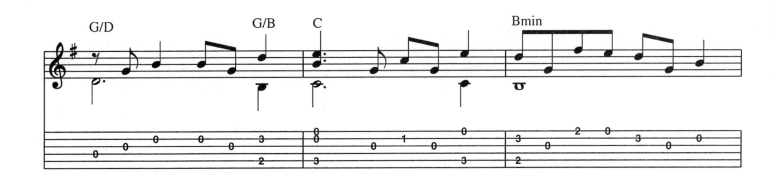

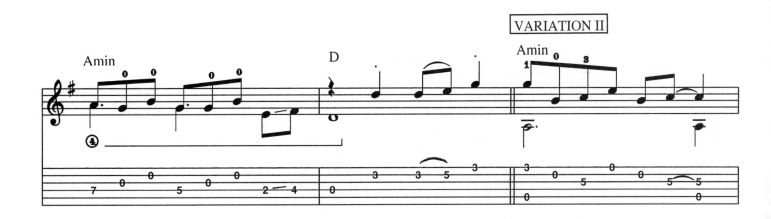

VARIATION II

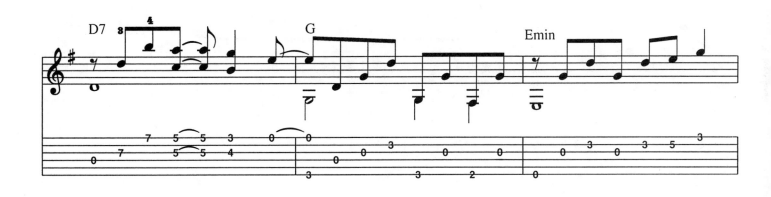

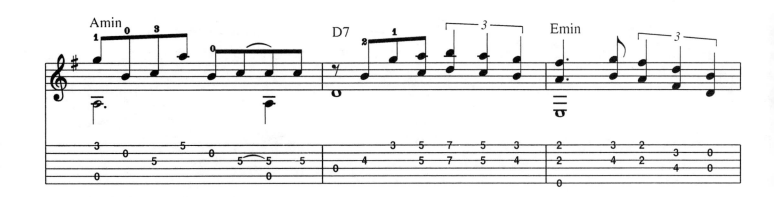

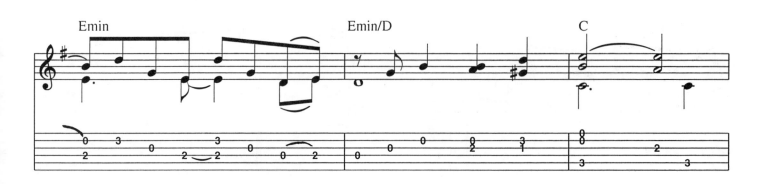

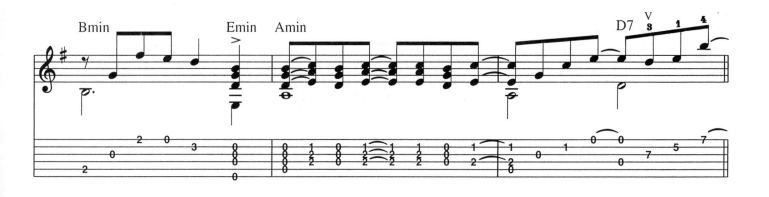

VARIATION III

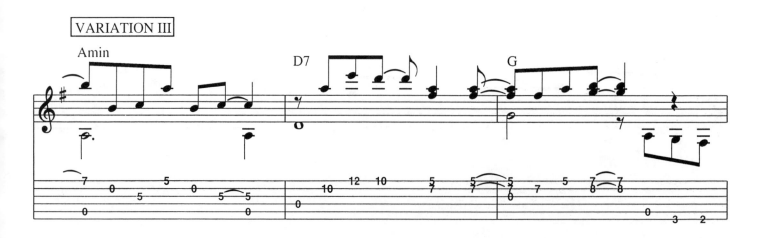

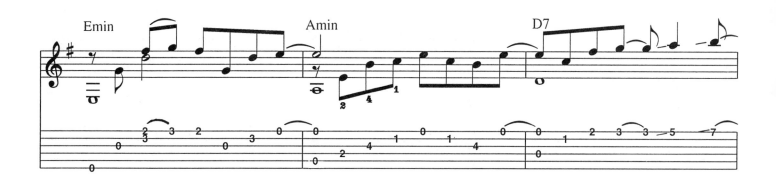

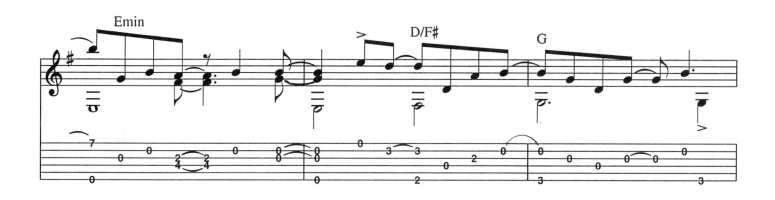

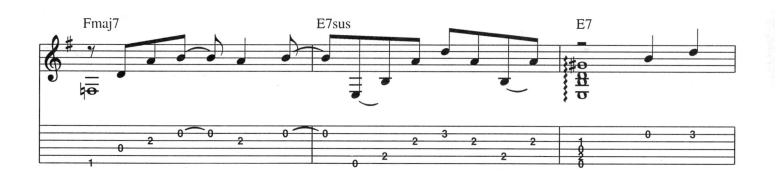

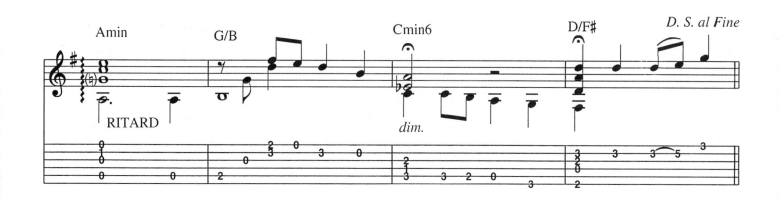

Shady Grove

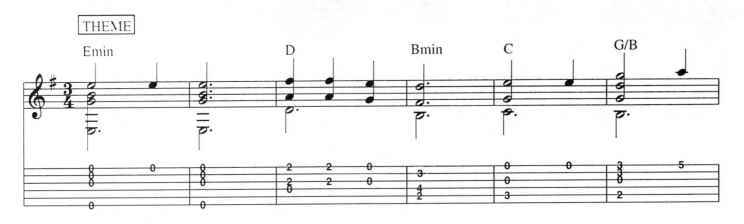

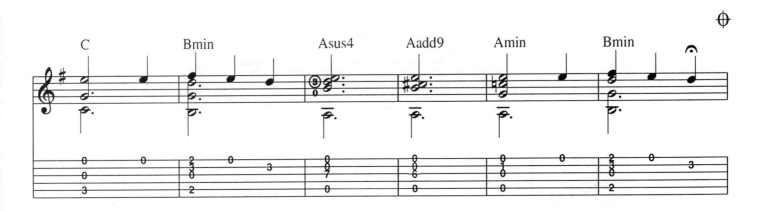

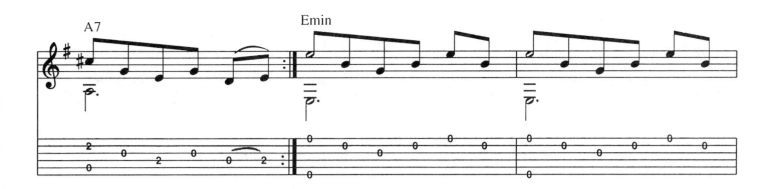

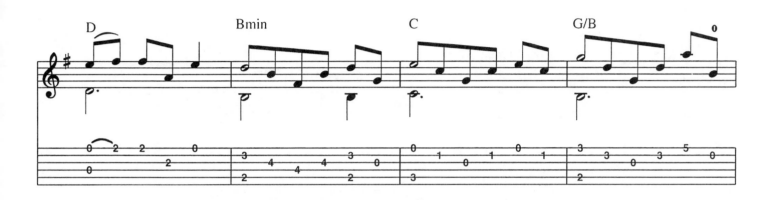

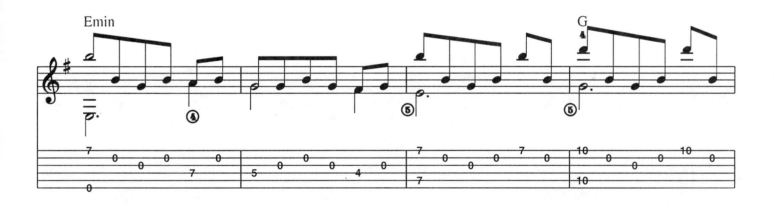

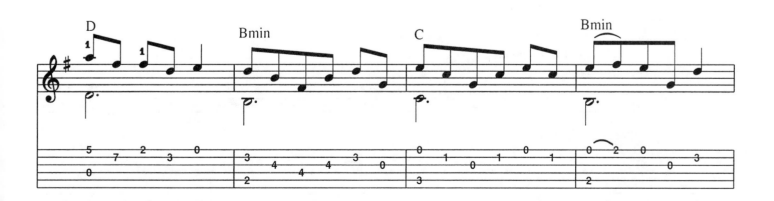

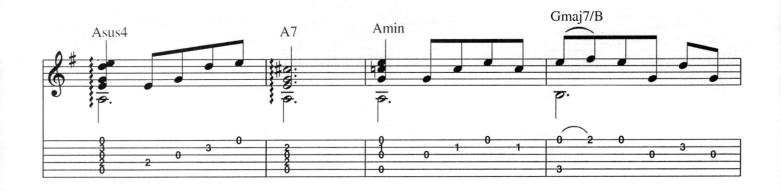

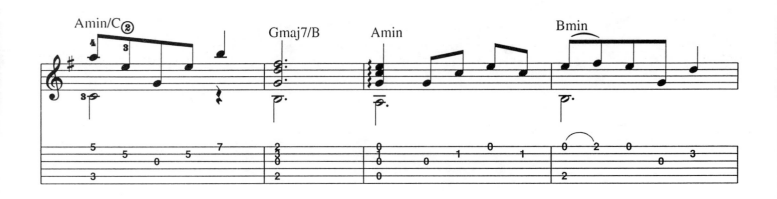

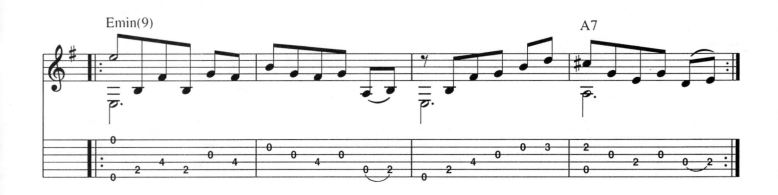

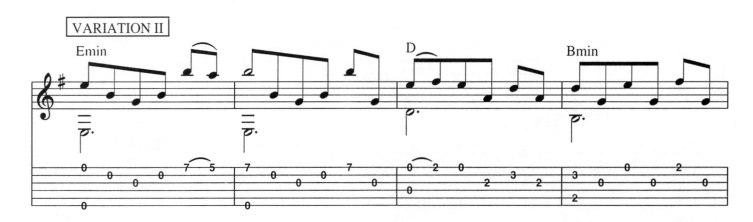

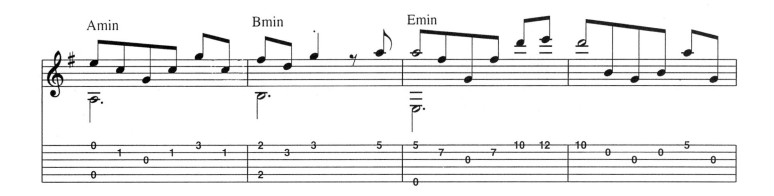

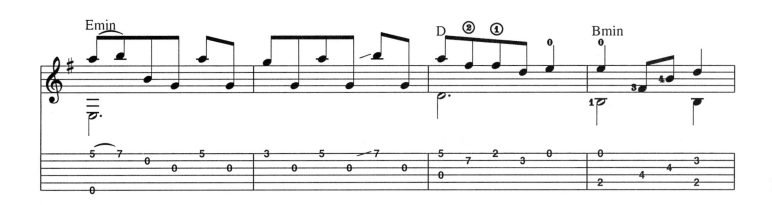

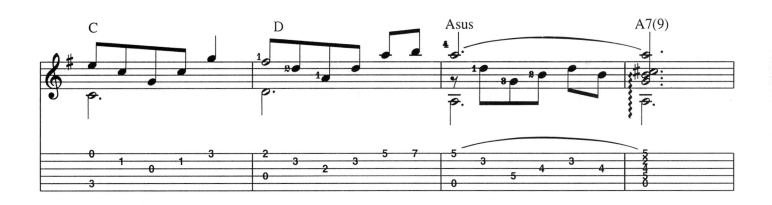

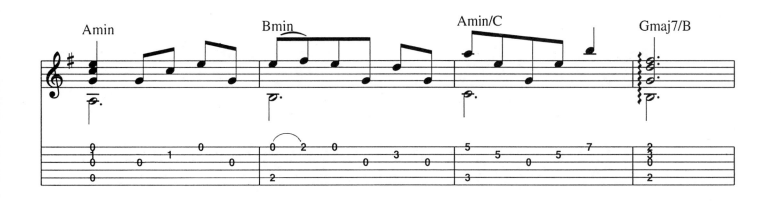

VARIATION III

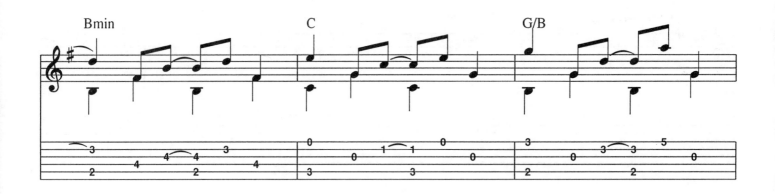

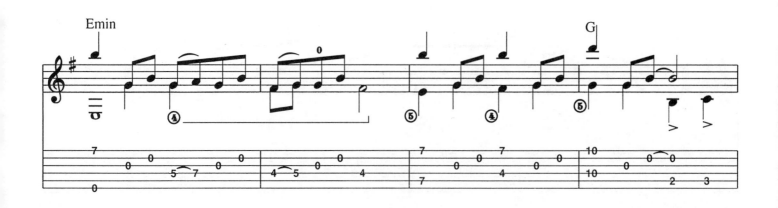

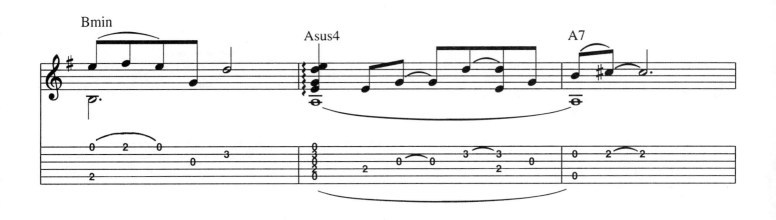

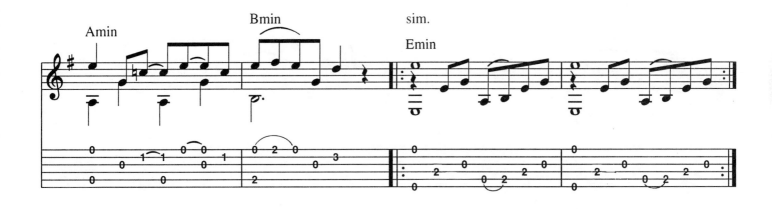

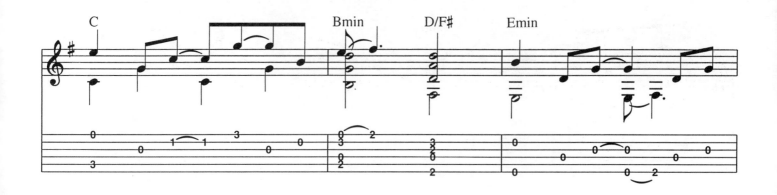

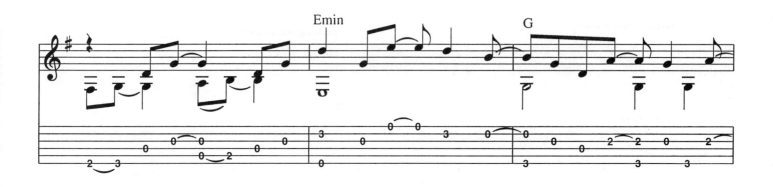

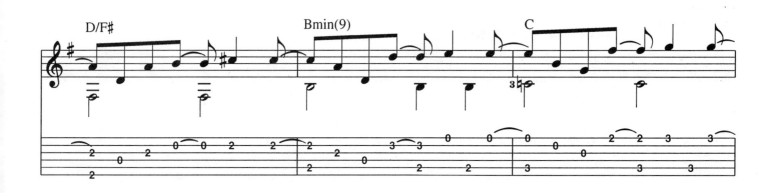

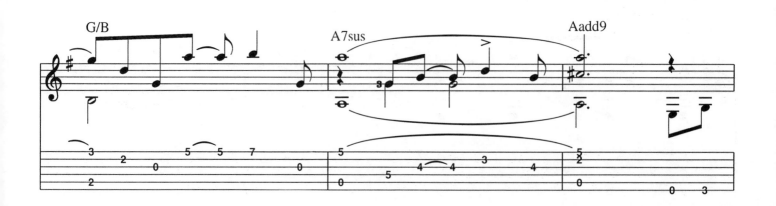

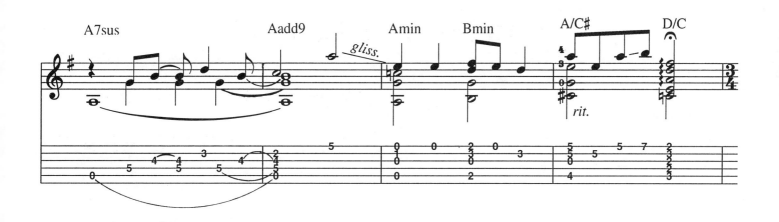

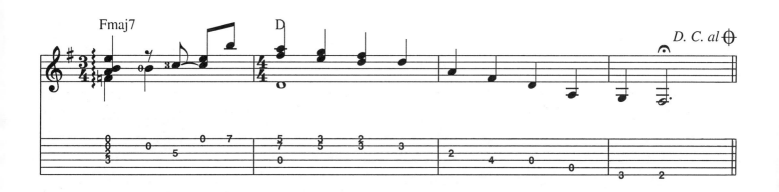

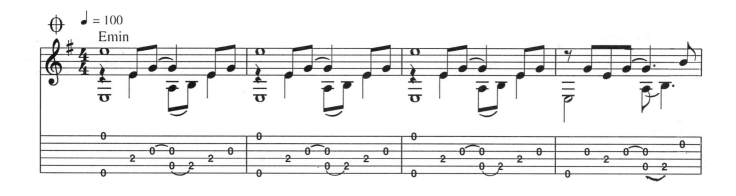

Down in the Valley

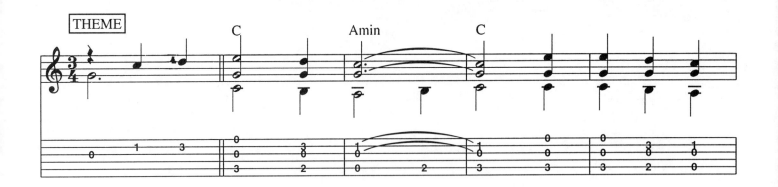

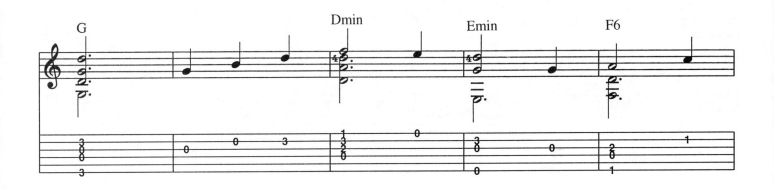

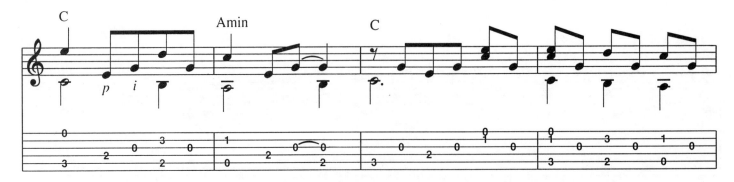

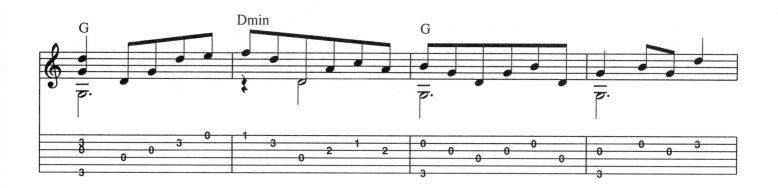

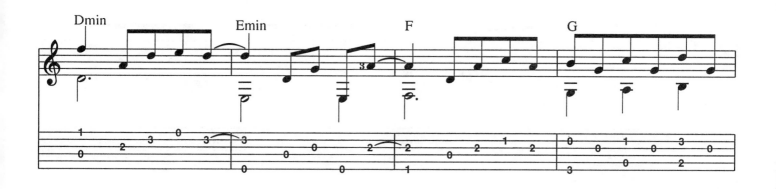

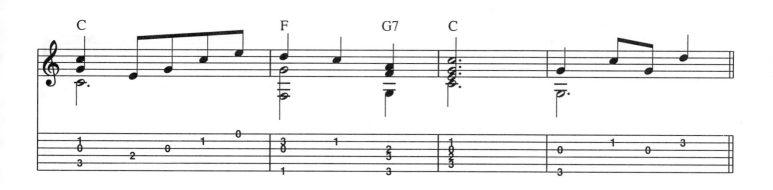

VARIATION II

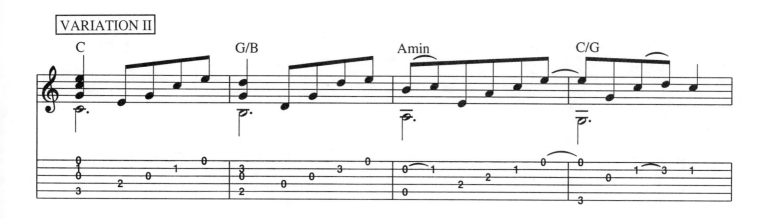

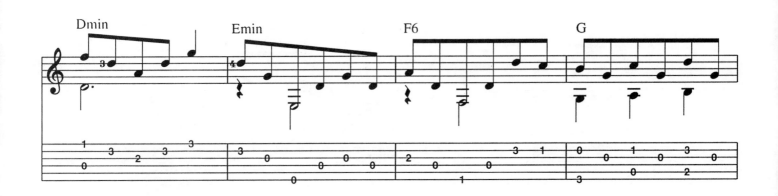

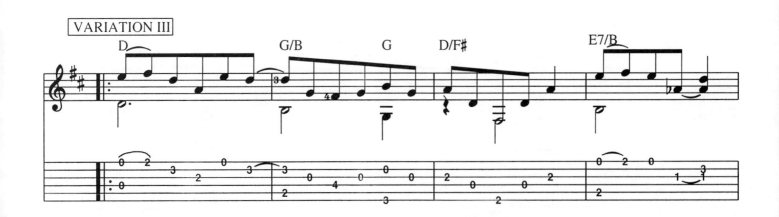

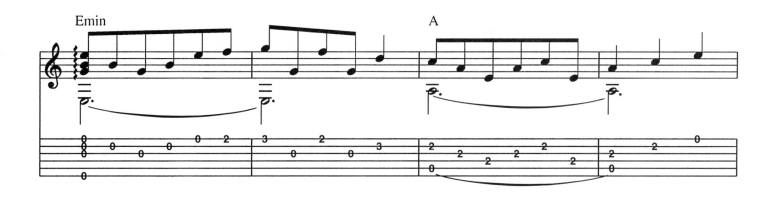

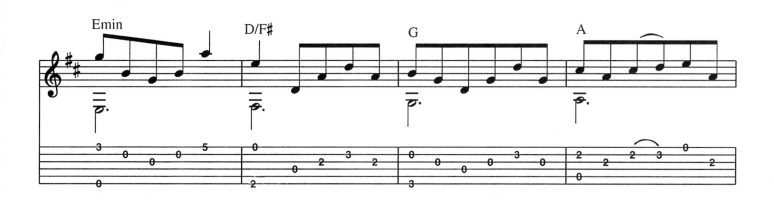

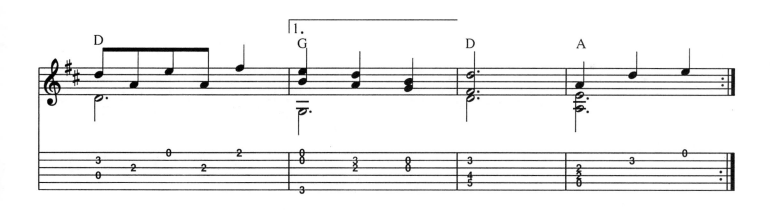

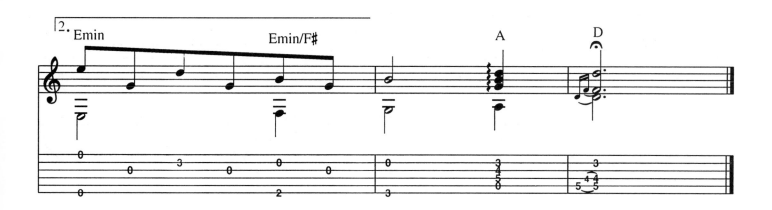

Red River Valley

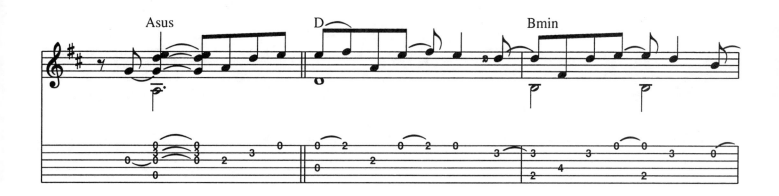

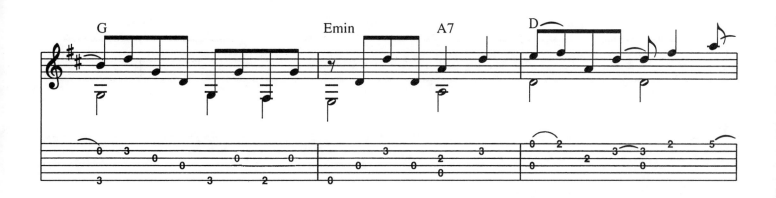

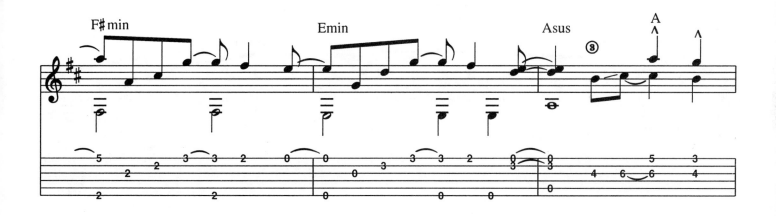

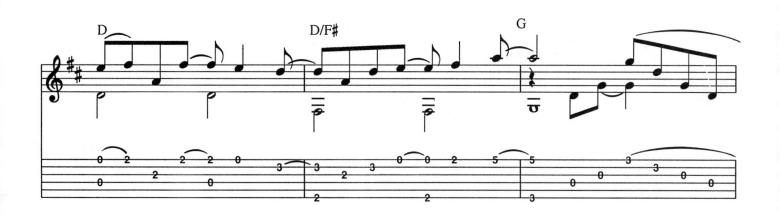

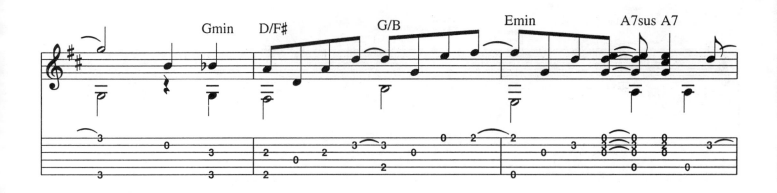

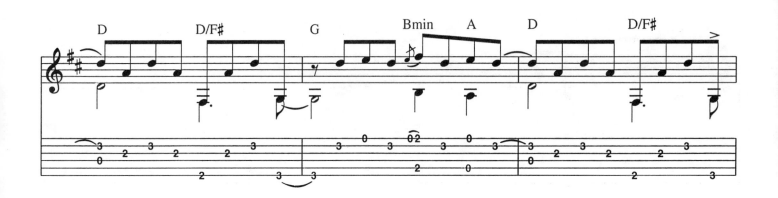

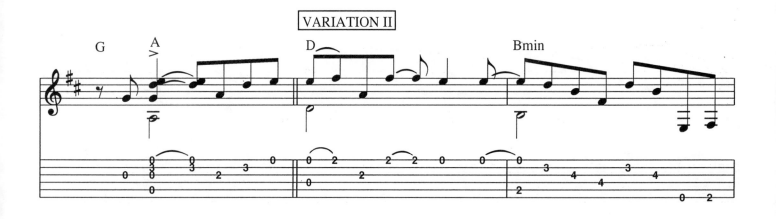

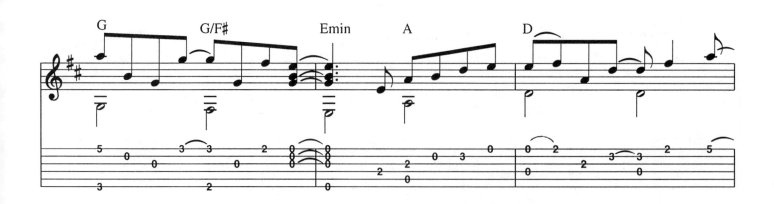

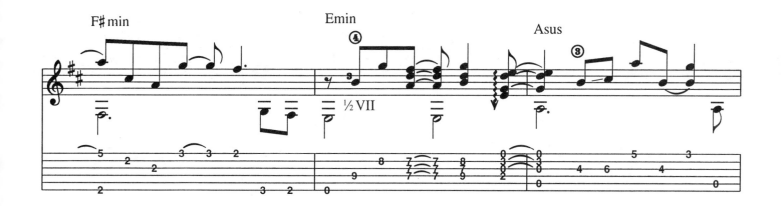

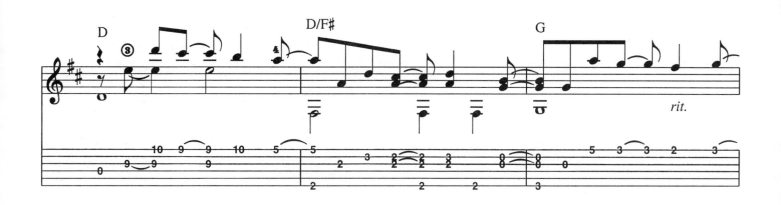

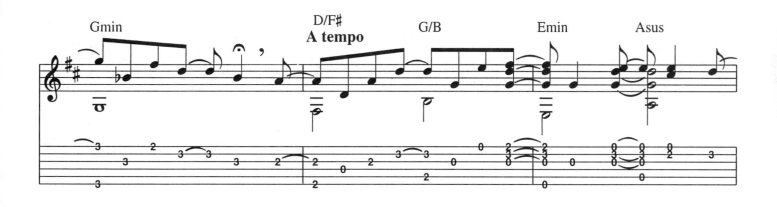

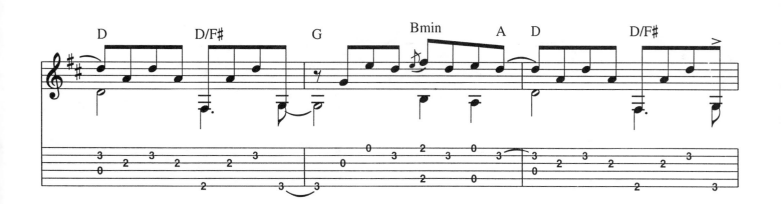

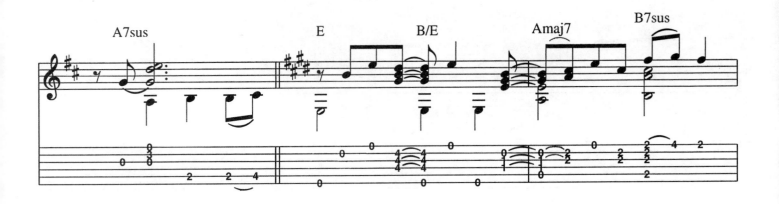

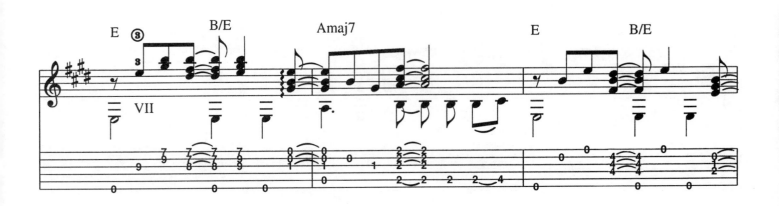

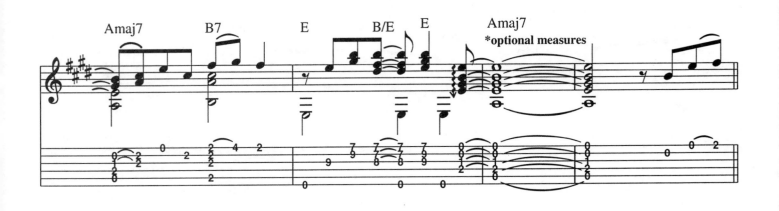

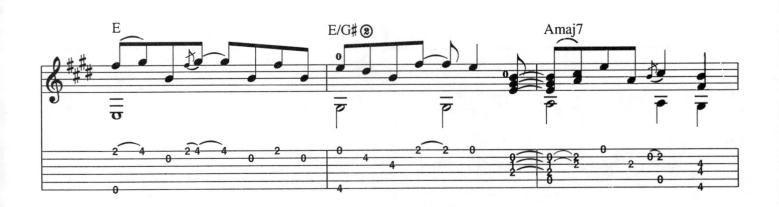

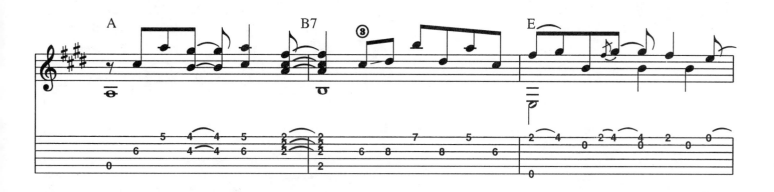

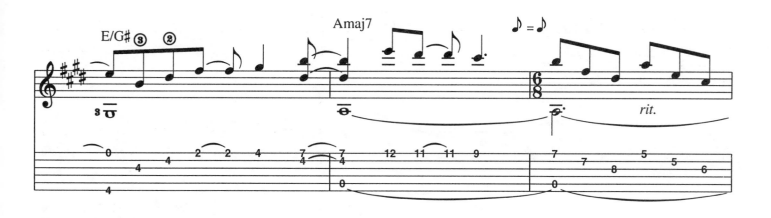

Medley: Cindy/Sweet Liza Jane

"Sweet Liza Jane"

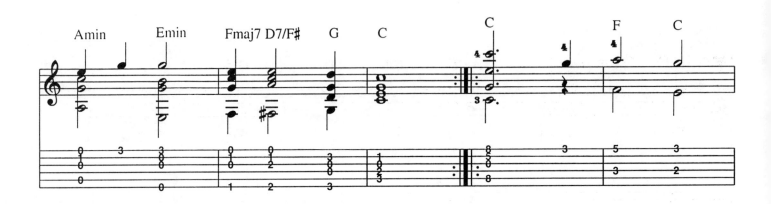

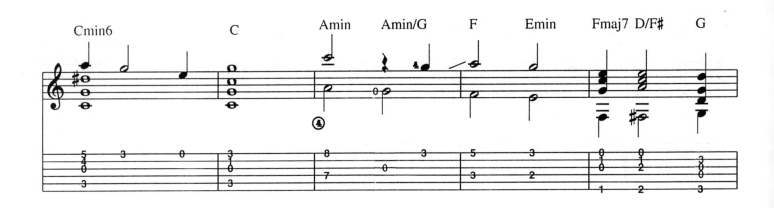

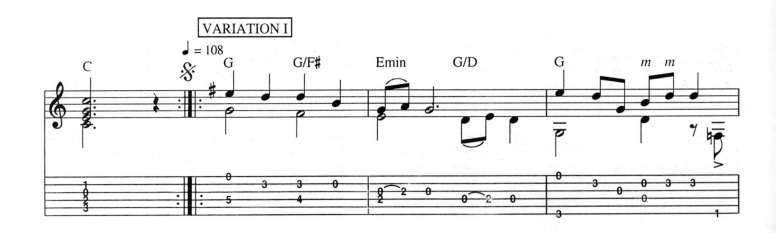

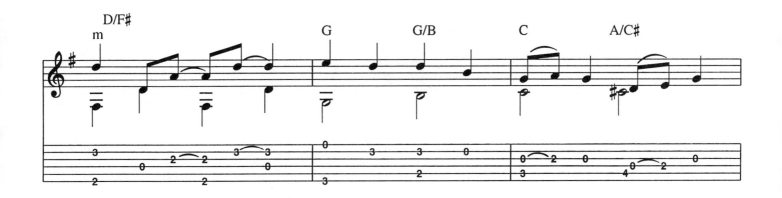

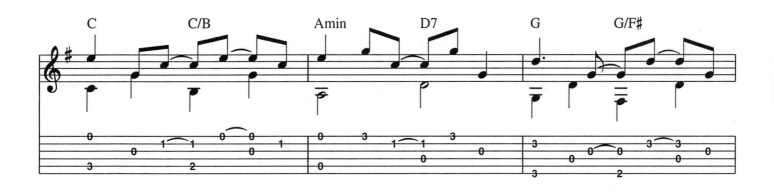

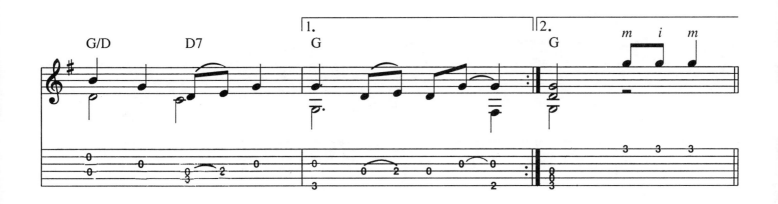

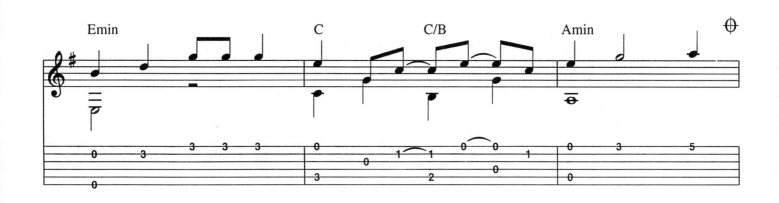

59

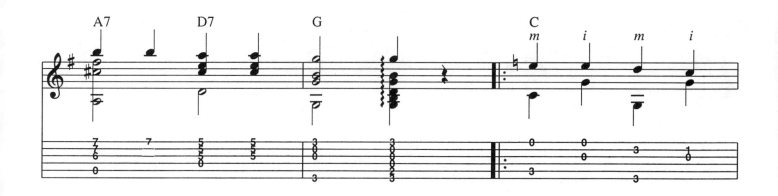

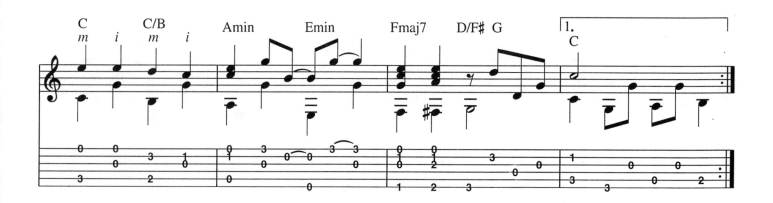

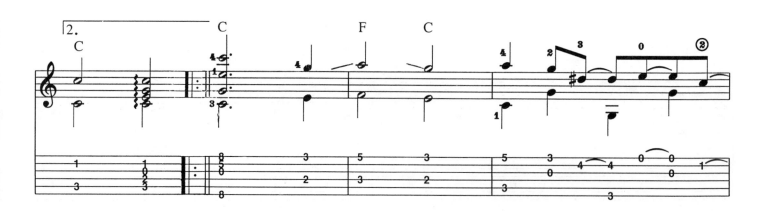

*Use back of the hand.

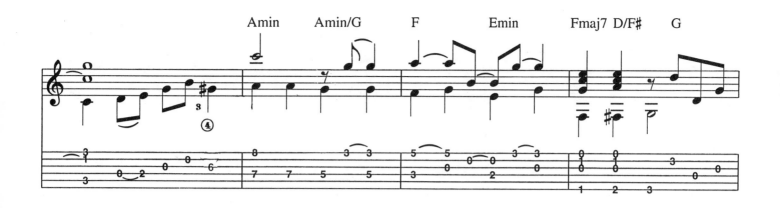

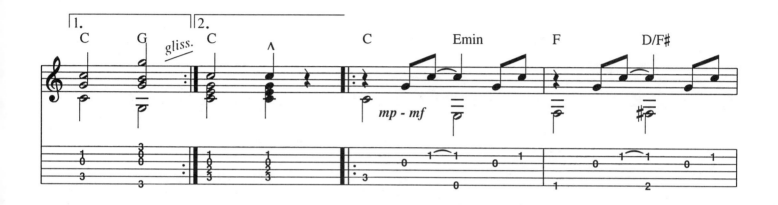

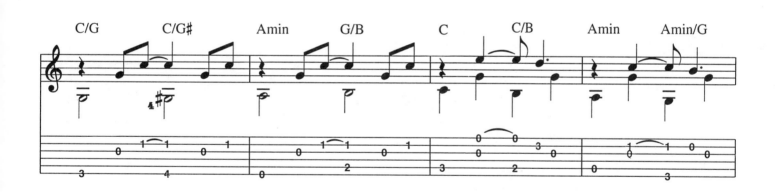

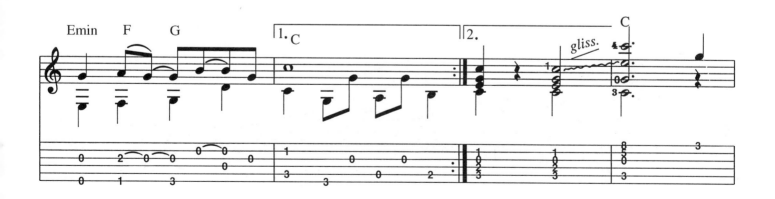

*Fingered in 4ths with 3rd and 4th fingers.